READING
SKILLS BOOK

LEVEL 6

Birthday girl

Answer in sentences.

"I told lots of people about my birthday. I had four surprise birthday messages. I was very happy."

1 Who is speaking?

2 What is the title of the story?

3 Who sent the birthday messages? Write down their names and say what the surprise was.

Comprehension

David's party

"Dad wanted to borrow some garden shears. He asked me to telephone Mr Small but I got mixed up."

1   Who is speaking?

2   What is the title of the story?

3   What are the names of the people David should have telephoned? What should he have asked them to bring?

A capital letter is used to begin a sentence.

A capital letter is used for people's titles (Mr, Mrs, Miss, Ms, Dr).

It is used for the names of people and places,

for example, **David**, **London**.

A sentence ends with a full stop.

Copy the sentences and put in the capital letters and full stops.

1   dad wanted to borrow mr small's shears

2   david telephoned mrs green

3   mrs brown said david could borrow her stable

4   the baker brought david some buns

5   mr jones brought some plates and mops

6   mr tall brought some chairs

7   david told dad about the telephone calls

8   david and dad had a party

Calling names

Read the poem on page 22.

1   Make a list of the names that the brother is called.

2   Make a list of the names that the sister is called.

3   What does Mum call them both?

Look at the pictures on pages 22 and 23.

4   Why do you think the boy is called Waggle Ears?

5   Why do you think the girl is called Mop Head?

6   How do you think the children feel about being called names?

7   Do people call you a name? Write it down.

8   How do you feel about people calling you this name?

Answer in sentences.

1   What was Adam's bad habit? (page 24)

2   What did Adam call Elly Jenkins? (page 25)

3   What did Adam really want to do? (page 27)

4   Where and when did the children meet every day?
(page 27)

5   What do you think the children were talking about on page 27?

6   Think of a good nickname for Adam.

7   Write about a bad habit that you have.

8   Write about a good habit that you have.

Comprehension

The school un-fair

Copy out each sentence but leave out the words that are underlined.

Choose a word from the balloons to fill the gap.

Be careful! There are more words than you need.

1 All the children were <u>in a good mood</u> but Kay.

2 There were lots of <u>men, women and children</u> at the school.

3 A clown had come to the school to do <u>special tricks</u>.

4 "I <u>am not allowed to</u> help on the book stall," said Kay.

Weather balloons

Answer in sentences.

1   Why does the weather man fill the balloon with gas?

2   What does the balloon take up with it?

3   How does the weatherman get messages about the weather?

4   How can the weatherman tell which way the wind is blowing?

5   Do you think the weather balloon can go higher than a bird?

6   Who do you think needs to know about the weather?

The first balloon

Choose the best ending for each sentence. Write the whole sentence in your book.

1 The first balloons were made by
- (a) the King and Queen.
- (b) Joseph and Etienne Montgolfier.
- (c) the weathermen.

2 When Joseph filled a bag with hot air he found that
- (a) the bag floated up into the air.
- (b) the fire went out.
- (c) his clothes got hot.

3 The first ride in a balloon was made by
- (a) Joseph and his brother.
- (b) the King and Queen.
- (c) three animals.

4 Balloons that floated in the air meant that
- (a) at last people could fly in the sky.
- (b) people needed big fires.
- (c) people could go shopping.

5 A balloon came down and frightened people. They thought it was
- (a) an aeroplane.
- (b) a monster.
- (c) a bird.

Mum   Dad   Liz   Ben   Ajay   Kamla

1 Pretend that you are one of the characters in the story and write about your day out in London.

Write about:

• how you got to London.

• what you saw first when you got to London.

• what the pigeons did when you fed them.

• how you could tell if the queen was at home.

• where you had your picnic.

• where you went to last.

• how you got home.

• what the best thing was that you saw.

2 Draw pictures for your story.

Answer in sentences.

1 Read page 12. Find two interesting facts about snowflakes. Write them down.

2 Why do you get lots of snow on mountains?

3 Name two places that are always covered in ice and snow.

4 Write down two things that help some animals to live in the snow.

Answer in sentences.

1   Why was Ben fed up?

2   What were the three things that Ben wanted to do?

3   Why did the children take a tin tray to the park?

4   What did Ajay's dad tell the children to take up the hill?

5   What happened to the bin bag?

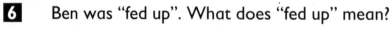

6   Ben was "fed up". What does "fed up" mean?

7   Why did Ben say that he had lost his feet?

8   How do you think Mr Jones felt when he saw the children looking cold, wet and sad?

9   How did Mr Jones make the children happy?

10   Why do you think the snow went grey?

Look at the words below. Some of the words are things that were given to little Joe. Some of the words are the names of the people who gave him the things. Some of the words are where little Joe put the things.

video machine

Sal   Keys

dustbin

book

sandwich

Tom   Dad

washing machine

Giant

Make three lists in your book to show who gave Joe the things, and where he put them. Like this:

Who?	What?	Where?
Sal	book	washing machine

The very proud elephant

Answer in sentences.

1 What was the elephant proud of?

2 What did each animal have that could win a prize?

3 What did each of the animals choose for a prize?

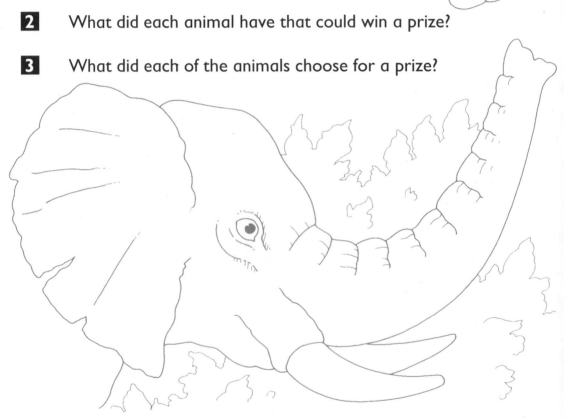

4 Why did the elephant think that bananas were a good prize?

5 Think of one more thing about each animal that makes them different from the others.

6 Which animal in the story do you like best? Say why.

Answer in sentences.

1   What was Susie playing with?

2   What did the little man do when Susie pressed the buttons?

3   What was in the cave that the little man fell into?

4   How did Susie try to help the little man?

5   What was strange about the little man in this video game?

6   How do you think Susie felt when the little man talked to her?

Machines, machines

1   This poem mentions the jobs that different machines do.
Using the pictures to help you, write down which machines you
think Wes Magee means when he says:

(a)   one hoovers the house

(b)   one dries your damp hair

(c)   some roar down the road

(d)   some orbit in space

(e)   one ticks in the hall

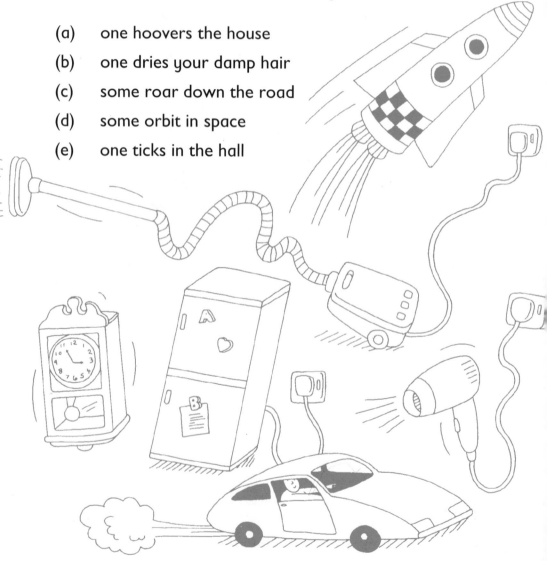

Machines, machines

2 Write down all the machines you can think of that might "hum while you sleep".

3 Think of some other machines and describe what they do. See if a friend can guess what they are.

Read the sentences and choose the best word from the box to say how the people felt. Write a sentence about how they felt.

1   Penny and Peter were on their way to school. They heard a funny noise. They went to see what it was. It was a robot!

How do you think they felt?

2   The robot was crying. "I am a rubbish robot. I am rubbish. I can't count."

How do you think the robot felt?

3   "A robot that can't count," laughed Penny.

"You see, you laughed at me," said the robot.

"No, we didn't," said Peter.

How do you think Peter felt?

4   The man from the recycling factory came to school.

He wanted to take Rupert back to work.

How do you think Rupert felt?

Answer in sentences.

1 Name the satellite that you can see on page 27.

2 Satellites can tell us about lots of things. Write down three things that they can tell us about.

3 Write down how long it takes for a television signal to get from a satellite to your television screen.

4 How far away from the earth are the satellites that carry television signals?

5 What happens to old satellites?

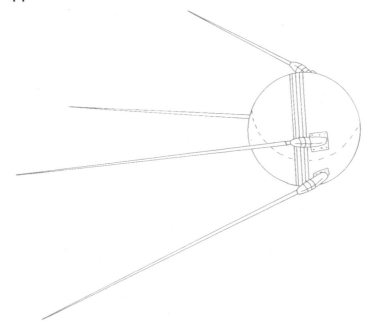

The boy and the wolf

The following sentences are not true.

Change the sentences so that they **are** true.

Use Book 6 to help you.

1 The boy liked to sit and watch his sheep. He thought it was good fun.

2 The boy shouted to two men but they didn't hear him.

3 The men laughed when they found out that the boy had played a trick on them.

4 The boy decided not to play his trick again.

Comprehension

5 When the wolf did come to eat the sheep, the men chased it away.

6 The wolf said that playing tricks on people made them help you.

Read the story of the boy and the wolf again. What do you think happens next? Draw a picture in your book to show what happened. Now write your ending to the story in your book.

The little red hen

Answer in sentences.

1 Where did the little red hen live?

2 What did she do when all her work was done?

3 Why did the fox hide behind the tree?

4 What did the little red hen do when the fox jumped out from behind the tree?

5 Why didn't the fox catch the hen when she fell out of the tree?

6 What could the little red hen have done so that she didn't get dizzy?

7 Do you think the fox chasing his tail was a good way to try to catch the little red hen?

8 Do you think the fox will try to catch the little red hen again?

Answer in sentences.

1   What did the Wind and the Sun have to do for their competition?

2   What did the North Wind do to try and win?

3   What did the Sun do to try and win?

4   Why did the man pull his coat tightly round him?

5   How did the Sun make the man take his coat off?

6   What was the weather like when the North Wind was blowing?

7   How do you think the North Wind felt at the end of the story?

8   Do you think the Sun knew she would win? Why?

Answer in sentences.

1 What would you say if you were the fairy in the story "The vinegar bottle"? Write about why you made the old woman's wishes come true. How did you feel when she didn't like living in the palace?

2 What would you say if you were the fox in the story "The little red hen"? Write about why you wanted to catch her. Why did your plan go wrong?

3 What would you say if you were the Sun in the story "The Wind and the Sun"? Write about the competition you thought of. How did you feel when you won?

Responding to reading